GCSE English Literature AQA Anthology

Place

The Workbook
Higher Level

This book will help you prepare for the Anthology
part of your GCSE English Literature exam.

It contains lots of questions designed to make you an
expert on writing about poetry.

It's ideal for use as a homework book or to help you revise.

What CGP is all about

Our sole aim here at CGP is to produce the highest quality
books — carefully written, immaculately presented and
dangerously close to being funny.

Then we work our socks off to get them out to you
— at the cheapest possible prices.

CONTENTS

Section One — Poems from the Literary Heritage

Section Two — Contemporary Poems

Section Three — Themes

Section Four — Analysing Answers

Published by Coordination Group Publications Ltd.

Editors:
Rachael Powers, Edward Robinson, Hayley Thompson

Produced with:
Alison Smith, Peter Thomas, Nicola Woodfin

Contributors:
Elisabeth Sanderson, Alison Smith

With thanks to Heather Gregson and Pam Jenkins for the proofreading
and Jan Greenway for the copyright research.

ISBN: 978 1 84762 538 0
Groovy website: www.cgpbooks.co.uk
Jolly bits of clipart from CorelDRAW®
Printed by Elanders Hindson Ltd, Newcastle upon Tyne

Based on the classic CGP style created by Richard Parsons.

Photocopying — it's dull, it takes ages… and sometimes it's a bit naughty. Luckily, it's dead cheap, easy and
quick to order more copies of this book from CGP — just call us on 0870 750 1242. Phew!

How to Use this Book

This book is for anyone studying the <u>Place</u> cluster of the AQA GCSE English Literature <u>Poetry Anthology</u>. It's got loads of <u>questions</u> in it to help you get your head around the poems.

Sections One and Two are About the Poems

There's a double page on each poem. It looks a bit like this:

There's some info about the <u>poet</u> here.

There's plenty of <u>space</u> around the poem for you to make <u>notes</u>.

Difficult words are defined in the <u>Poem Dictionary</u>.

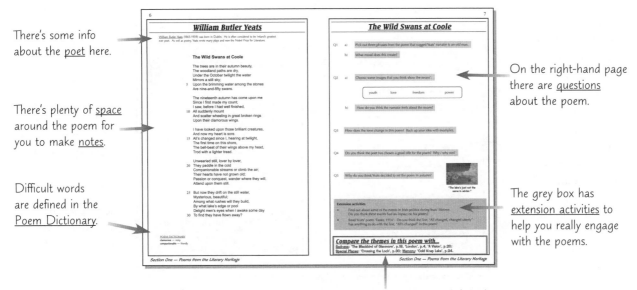

On the right-hand page there are <u>questions</u> about the poem.

The grey box has <u>extension activities</u> to help you really engage with the poems.

The top tip box lists some of the <u>other</u> <u>poems</u> in the cluster with <u>similar themes</u>.

A little bit about the questions...

This is the most important bit...

1) The questions are designed to get you <u>thinking for yourself</u> about the poem.
2) They start off nice and <u>simple</u>, then get <u>trickier</u> as you go down the page.
3) Answer the questions as <u>thoroughly</u> as you can.
   It's important to get to know the poems <u>inside out</u>.
4) The answers can be found in the <u>separate answer book</u>.

The questions in these two sections mostly ask you about <u>technical</u> stuff like <u>language</u>, <u>structure</u> and <u>form</u>.

How to Use this Book

Comparing the poems is one of the most important things you'll have to do — that's what Section Three is all about. The questions in it will help you link the different poems by their themes.

Section Three is About the Themes

A double page spread in the Themes section looks a bit like this:

A different theme is covered on each page.

There are questions about the theme and how different poems relate to it.

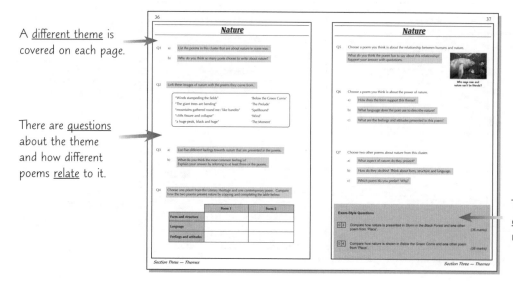

The grey box has exam-style questions relating to the themes.

This is a Really Useful Section

1) The questions are designed to get you thinking about the poems' themes and ideas.

2) They'll also get you to compare the poems — which is just what you'll need to do to get good marks in your exam.

3) The exam-style questions are exactly that — questions like the ones you'll get in your exam. Use them to practise planning and writing answers. Trust me, it'll really help when it comes to the real thing.

Remember: the themes covered in this section aren't the only ones you can write about — they're here to give you some ideas. Once you start thinking about the poems and comparing them with each other, you're bound to come up with a few more of your own.

How to Use this Book

One of the <u>best ways</u> to learn how to get marks is to <u>analyse</u> some <u>exam-style answers</u>. So that's what you'll be doing in Section Four. You <u>lucky thing</u>, you.

Section Four lets you Analyse some Answers

A page in Section Four might look a bit like this:

These instructions tell you what you have to do (more on this below).

This is a sample extract from a student's answer.

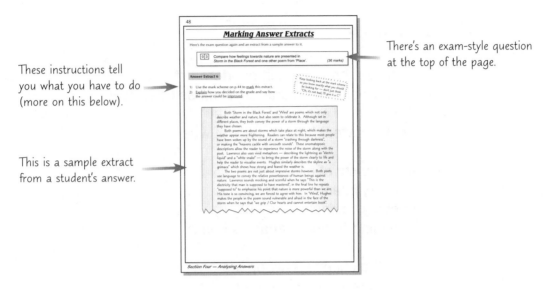

There's an exam-style question at the top of the page.

This Section Helps You Understand How to Do Well

1) Most of the questions in this section ask you to <u>grade</u> a <u>sample exam answer</u>.

2) They'll also ask you to say what the student needs to do to <u>score more marks</u> — this will help you understand how to <u>improve</u> your own answers.

3) Some of the questions ask you to <u>extend a point</u> or <u>give a quote</u> from the poem to back up a point. This helps you to understand how to really <u>use the poems</u> to write a top-notch answer.

> <u>Remember</u>: there's <u>more than one right answer</u> to the questions that you'll get in your poetry exam. These sample answers are just designed to show you the <u>kind of points</u> you'll need to make and the <u>kind of writing style</u> you'll need to use to get a top grade.

William Blake

William Blake (1757-1827) was born in London and educated at home by his mother. He was a poet, artist, engraver and publisher. He believed in the power of the imagination and religion over materialism.

London

I wander through each chartered street,
Near where the chartered Thames does flow,
And mark in every face I meet
Marks of weakness, marks of woe.

5   In every cry of every man,
In every infant's cry of fear,
In every voice, in every ban,
The mind-forged manacles I hear:

How the chimney-sweeper's cry
10 Every black'ning church appalls,
And the hapless soldier's sigh
Runs in blood down palace-walls.

But most through midnight streets I hear
How the youthful harlot's curse
15 Blasts the new-born infant's tear,
And blights with plagues the marriage hearse.

POEM DICTIONARY
chartered — rented out or organised for business purposes
woe — sadness
ban — a curse
manacles — handcuffs
harlot — a prostitute

London

Q1 a)   What is the rhyme scheme in this poem?

   b)   What effect does it create?

Q2   Find two examples of repetition in the poem. What effect does this repetition have?

Q3   Copy out the table below and fill it in using three different emotive images from the poem. Explain the effect each image has on the reader.

Image	Effect
"youthful harlot"	Suggests loss of youthful innocence

Here's one to start you off.

Q4   How does Blake's emotive language convey his feelings about society?

This is just language that makes you feel a particular emotion.

Q5   Why do you think Blake wrote this poem in the first person?

Writing in the first person means using words like "I" and "me".

Q6   What do you think Blake means by the phrase: "mind-forged manacles"?

Q7   Why do you think Blake decided to write this poem?

Extension activity

•   Find some images of London in the 18th and 19th centuries. Compare the pictures with Blake's descriptions and say whether you agree with his view of the city at that time.

Other poems touch on these themes...

Bitterness and Anger: 'A Vision', p.20, 'Neighbours', p.28; Urban Life: 'Hard Water', p.32.

William Butler Yeats

William Butler Yeats (1865-1939) was born in Dublin. He is often considered to be Ireland's greatest ever poet. As well as poetry, Yeats wrote many plays and won the Nobel Prize for Literature.

The Wild Swans at Coole

The trees are in their autumn beauty,
The woodland paths are dry,
Under the October twilight the water
Mirrors a still sky;
5 Upon the brimming water among the stones
Are nine-and-fifty swans.

The nineteenth autumn has come upon me
Since I first made my count;
I saw, before I had well finished,
10 All suddenly mount
And scatter wheeling in great broken rings
Upon their clamorous wings.

I have looked upon those brilliant creatures,
And now my heart is sore.
15 All's changed since I, hearing at twilight,
The first time on this shore,
The bell-beat of their wings above my head,
Trod with a lighter tread.

Unwearied still, lover by lover,
20 They paddle in the cold
Companionable streams or climb the air;
Their hearts have not grown old;
Passion or conquest, wander where they will,
Attend upon them still.

25 But now they drift on the still water,
Mysterious, beautiful;
Among what rushes will they build,
By what lake's edge or pool
Delight men's eyes when I awake some day
30 To find they have flown away?

POEM DICTIONARY
clamorous — noisy
companionable — friendly

ummary

The Wild Swans at Coole

Q1 a) Pick out three phrases from the poem that suggest Yeats' narrator is an old man.

b) What mood does this create?

Q2 a) Choose some images that you think show the swans':

> youth   love   freedom   power

b) How do you think the narrator feels about the swans?

Q3 How does the tone change in this poem? Back up your idea with examples.

Q4 Do you think the poet has chosen a good title for the poem? Why / why not?

Q5 Why do you think Yeats decided to set the poem in autumn?

"The lake's just not the same in winter."

Extension activities

- Find out about some of the events in Irish politics during Yeats' lifetime. Do you think these events had an impact on his poetry?

- Read Yeats' poem 'Easter, 1916'. Do you think the line, "All changed, changed utterly" has anything to do with the line, "All's changed" in this poem?

Compare the themes in this poem with...

Sadness: 'The Blackbird of Glanmore', p.18, 'London', p.4, 'A Vision', p.20;
Special Places: 'Crossing the Loch', p.30; **Memory:** 'Cold Knap Lake', p.24.

Section One — Poems from the Literary Heritage

William Wordsworth

<u>William Wordsworth</u> (1770-1850) was one of England's greatest poets.
He was born in Cockermouth, and wrote many poems about the Lake District.

Extract from The Prelude

One summer evening (led by her) I found
A little boat tied to a willow tree
Within a rocky cave, its usual home.
Straight I unloosed her chain, and stepping in
5   Pushed from the shore. It was an act of stealth
And troubled pleasure, nor without the voice
Of mountain-echoes did my boat move on;
Leaving behind her still, on either side,
Small circles glittering idly in the moon,
10   Until they melted all into one track
Of sparkling light. But now, like one who rows,
Proud of his skill, to reach a chosen point
With an unswerving line, I fixed my view
Upon the summit of a craggy ridge,
15   The horizon's utmost boundary; far above
Was nothing but the stars and the grey sky.
She was an elfin pinnace; lustily
I dipped my oars into the silent lake,
And, as I rose upon the stroke, my boat
20   Went heaving through the water like a swan;
When, from behind that craggy steep till then
The horizon's bound, a huge peak, black and huge,
As if with voluntary power instinct,
Upreared its head. I struck and struck again,
25   And growing still in stature the grim shape
Towered up between me and the stars, and still,
For so it seemed, with purpose of its own
And measured motion like a living thing,
Strode after me. With trembling oars I turned,
30   And through the silent water stole my way
Back to the covert of the willow tree;
There in her mooring-place I left my bark, –
And through the meadows homeward went, in grave
And serious mood; but after I had seen
35   That spectacle, for many days, my brain
Worked with a dim and undetermined sense
Of unknown modes of being; o'er my thoughts
There hung a darkness, call it solitude
Or blank desertion. No familiar shapes
40   Remained, no pleasant images of trees,
Of sea or sky, no colours of green fields;
But huge and mighty forms, that do not live
Like living men, moved slowly through the mind
By day, and were a trouble to my dreams.

<u>POEM DICTIONARY</u>
stealth — secrecy
pinnace — a kind of
old sailing boat
lustily — enthusiastically
covert — shelter

The Prelude

Q1   a)   Pick out three phrases from lines 1-20 that suggest the narrator is feeling content.

       b)   Is there anything in lines 1-20 that indicates the mood is about to change?

Q2   a)   Choose three phrases from lines 21-44 that suggest the narrator's mood has changed.

       b)   How do you think the narrator feels in these lines?

Q3   When the narrator says that the mountain, "with purpose of its own... / Strode after me", he gives it a human personality.

       a)   What is this technique called? Choose the correct word below:

             personification   objectification   contrast

       b)   What effect does this have?

Q4   Why do you think the poet has chosen to write in blank verse? What effect does it have?

> Blank verse is poetry that doesn't rhyme, but has a regular rhythm.

Q5   How does Wordsworth present his ideas about the following themes?

       a)   nature
       b)   man's relationship with nature

Extension activities

- Read a bit more of 'The Prelude', or some of Wordsworth's other poems. How do you think the ideas in this extract fit in with the rest of his work?

- Do you think this poem is autobiographical? Why / why not?

Other poems have similar themes...

Life-changing Moments: 'Below the Green Corrie', p.12; Mankind vs Nature: 'Wind', p.16, 'The Moment', p.22; The Power of Nature: 'Storm in the Black Forest', p.14.

Emily Brontë

Emily Brontë (1818-1848) was born in Yorkshire, one of the three famous Brontë sisters.
After studying for a time in Brussels, the sisters published a collection of their poetry under pseudonyms
(Emily's being 'Ellis Bell') to avoid discrimination against female writers.

Spellbound

The night is darkening round me,
The wild winds coldly blow;
But a tyrant spell has bound me
And I cannot, cannot go.

5   The giant trees are bending
Their bare boughs weighed with snow.
And the storm is fast descending,
And yet I cannot go.

Clouds beyond clouds above me,
10 Wastes beyond wastes below;
But nothing drear can move me;
I will not, cannot go.

POEM DICTIONARY
tyrant — a cruel ruler or dictator
drear — dreary, gloomy

Spellbound

Q1 a) What is the rhyme scheme in this poem?

b) Why do you think the poet has chosen this rhyme scheme?

Q2 Some of the phrases in this poem contain words that start
with the same consonant, e.g. "wild winds" and "bare boughs".

a) What is this called? Choose the correct answer from the following options:

assonance   alliteration   caesura

b) What effect does it help to create in this poem?

Q3 Find three images of the storm's power. What impression do these images give you of the storm?

Q4 Find three examples of repetition in the poem. What is their overall effect?

Q5 Look at lines 4 and 8.

a) What do you think the narrator means?

Now look at line 12.

b) What do you think she means now? Is there a difference?

The overall effect of
Katie's repetitions was
nicely toned arms.

Extension activities

• What impression do you get of the poem's narrator?

• What do you think the ideas behind this poem are?
  Is it just a poem about a storm or do you think it could have a deeper meaning?

Other poems touch on these themes...

The Magic of Nature: 'Crossing the Loch', p.30, 'Below the Green Corrie', p.12;
The Power of a Storm: 'Storm in the Black Forest', p.14, 'Wind', p.16.

Norman MacCaig

Norman MacCaig (1910-1996) was a Scottish poet born in Edinburgh. He started out as a primary school teacher, later working for the University of Stirling in Scotland and publishing several works of poetry. He won the Queen's Gold Medal for Poetry in 1985.

Below the Green Corrie

The mountains gathered round me
like bandits. Their leader
swaggered up close in the dark light,
full of threats, full of thunders.

5   But it was they who stood and delivered.
They gave me their money and their lives.
They filled me with mountains and thunders.

My life was enriched
with an infusion of theirs.
10 I clambered downhill through the ugly weather.
And when I turned to look goodbye
to those marvellous prowlers
a sunshaft had pierced the clouds
and their leader,
15 that swashbuckling mountain,
was wearing
a bandolier of light.

A marvellous growler

POEM DICTIONARY
Corrie — a hollow on a mountainside
bandolier — an over-the-shoulder belt that normally holds gun cartridges
swashbuckling — wild, adventurous

Below the Green Corrie

Q1   What would you associate with a "Green Corrie"?

Q2   a)   What is the atmosphere in the first stanza? How is it created?

      b)   How does the mood change in the second stanza?

Q3   Pick out an image in the first two stanzas that you find interesting or funny.
      Explain its effect on you.

Q4   The narrator says, "My life was enriched / with an infusion of theirs."

      What do you think he means by this?

Q5   Pick out some images that MacCaig uses to describe the mountains in the final stanza.
      What impression do these images give you of the mountains now?

Q6   Why do you think the poet has chosen to describe the mountains as "bandits"?

Extension activities

- Imagine the story in this poem is being made into a comic strip.
  Choose a more exciting title for it that presents the idea of the mountains as bandits.

- Draw out a simple comic strip summarising the events in the poem.
  Make up some captions to go with the pictures.

Compare the themes of this poem with...
Life-changing Moments: 'The Prelude', p.8; **Awe of Nature:** 'Storm in the Black Forest', p.14;
Relationships with Nature: 'The Blackbird of Glanmore', p.18, 'The Wild Swans at Coole', p.6.

D H Lawrence

<u>David Herbert Lawrence</u> (1885-1930) was born in a mining town in Nottinghamshire, before moving to London to start a career in teaching. Following an illness in 1911, he left his job to become a full time writer and later travelled the world extensively.

Storm in the Black Forest

Now it is almost night, from the bronzey soft sky
jugfull after jugfull of pure white liquid fire, bright white
tipples over and spills down,
and is gone
5   and gold-bronze flutters bent through the thick upper air.

And as the electric liquid pours out, sometimes
a still brighter white snake wriggles among it, spilled
and tumbling wriggling down the sky:
and then the heavens cackle with uncouth sounds.

10   And the rain won't come, the rain refuses to come!

This is the electricity that man is supposed to have mastered
chained, subjugated to his use!
supposed to!

Storm in a teacup

<u>POEM DICTIONARY</u>
uncouth — rude
subjugated — brought under control

Section One — Poems from the Literary Heritage

Storm in the Black Forest

Q1 How does the poet set the scene at the start of the poem?

Q2 Copy out the table below and fill it in, giving two examples of the poet's use of colour. For each colour, explain the effect you think it has.

Colour	Effect
"bronzey"	sounds soft and hazy

Here's one to start you off.

Q3 Some of the sentences in this poem run over from one line onto the next.

a) What is this called? Choose the correct answer from the following options:

alliteration   caesura   enjambment

b) What effect does it create in this poem?

Q4 a) Find an example of onomatopoeia.

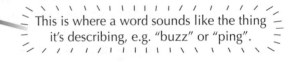

This is where a word sounds like the thing it's describing, e.g. "buzz" or "ping".

b) What effect does it have?

Q5 a) What point do you think the narrator is making in lines 11 to 13?

b) What do you think the overall message of the poem is?

Extension activities

- D H Lawrence lived through Britain's Industrial Revolution. Do some research on this period. Do you think this poem has something to say about it? If so, what?
- The word "tipples" has a different meaning from usual. Write down what you think it means here.

Other poems touch on these themes...
The Power of Nature: 'The Prelude', p.8, 'Wind', p.16; **The Magic of Nature:** 'Spellbound', p.10, 'Crossing the Loch', p.30; **Mankind vs Nature:** 'Below the Green Corrie', p.12, 'The Moment', p.22.

Ted Hughes

Ted Hughes (1930-1998) served as the British Poet Laureate from 1984 until he died. Born in West Yorkshire, he studied at Pembroke College, Cambridge, later spending most of his life in Devon.

Wind

This house has been far out at sea all night,
The woods crashing through darkness, the booming hills,
Winds stampeding the fields under the window
Floundering black astride and blinding wet

5   Till day rose; then under an orange sky
The hills had new places, and wind wielded
Blade-light, luminous black and emerald,
Flexing like the lens of a mad eye.

At noon I scaled along the house-side as far as
10   The coal-house door. Once I looked up -
Through the brunt wind that dented the balls of my eyes
The tent of the hills drummed and strained its guyrope,

The fields quivering, the skyline a grimace,
At any second to bang and vanish with a flap;
15   The wind flung a magpie away and a black-
Back gull bent like an iron bar slowly. The house

Rang like some fine green goblet in the note
That any second would shatter it. Now deep
In chairs, in front of the great fire, we grip
20   Our hearts and cannot entertain book, thought,

Or each other. We watch the fire blazing,
And feel the roots of the house move, but sit on,
Seeing the window tremble to come in,
Hearing the stones cry out under the horizons.

POEM DICTIONARY
wielded — used with skill
luminous — glowing
brunt — main force
guyrope — rope securing a tent to the ground

Wind

Q1   What do you think the narrator means when he says:
      "This house has been far out at sea all night"?

Q2   a)   The line "The tent of the hills drummed and strained its guyrope" is
            an example of what? Choose the correct answer from the following:

            a simile   a metaphor   an oxymoron

      b)   What does this line suggest about the storm?

This oxy-moron fell asleep
in the snow. Idiot.

Q3   Pick out three other images from the poem that you think describe the power
      of the storm effectively. For each image, say why you think it's effective.

Q4   How does Hughes present the people in this poem?
      Give examples to back up your ideas.

Q5   Do you think the title of this poem is effective? Why / why not?

Extension activity

- Some people have suggested that this poem is actually about a stormy relationship — possibly
  the poet's marriage to his first wife, Sylvia Plath. Other people think it's just a poem about a
  storm. Which point of view do you agree with? Find some evidence to back up your answer.

Several poems have similar themes...
The Power of Nature: 'Storm in the Black Forest', p.14, 'Spellbound', p.10; Mankind vs Nature:
'Below the Green Corrie', p.12, 'The Moment', p.22; Hopelessness: 'A Vision', p.20, 'London', p.4.

Section One — Poems from the Literary Heritage

Seamus Heaney

<u>Seamus Heaney</u> was born in 1939 in County Derry, Northern Ireland. He grew up on his father's farm before going to university in Belfast. His younger brother Christopher died in a road accident aged four.

The Blackbird of Glanmore

On the grass when I arrive,
Filling the stillness with life,
But ready to scare off
At the very first wrong move.
5   In the ivy when I leave.

It's you, blackbird, I love.

I park, pause, take heed.
Breathe. Just breathe and sit
And lines I once translated
10 Come back: 'I want away
To the house of death, to my father

Under the low clay roof.'

And I think of one gone to him,
A little stillness dancer –
15 Haunter-son, lost brother –
Cavorting through the yard,
So glad to see me home,

My homesick first term over.

And think of a neighbour's words
20 Long after the accident:
'Yon bird on the shed roof,
Up on the ridge for weeks –
I said nothing at the time

But I never liked yon bird.'

25 The automatic lock
Clunks shut, the blackbird's panic
Is shortlived, for a second
I've a bird's eye view of myself,
A shadow on raked gravel

30 In front of my house of life.

Hedge-hop, I am absolute
For you, your ready talkback,
Your each stand-offish comeback,
Your picky, nervy goldbeak -
35 On the grass when I arrive,

In the ivy when I leave.

POEM DICTIONARY
take heed — pay attention
cavorting — bouncing around
yon — that

The Blackbird of Glanmore

Q1   Find two images the narrator uses to describe the blackbird.
For each image, explain its effect on the reader.

Q2   Choose an image the narrator uses to describe his brother.
Do you think it's effective? Why / why not?

Q3   a)   What is the neighbour's view of the blackbird?

b)   Do you think the narrator agrees with this view? Explain your answer.

Q4   Look at line 8: "Breathe. Just breathe and sit".
The full stop after "Breathe" creates a break in the rhythm of the line.

a)   What is this technique called? Choose the correct answer from the following words:

caesura   enjambment   consonance

b)   Why do you think Heaney uses this technique here? What effect does it have?

Q5   What is the effect of the onomatopoeic word "Clunks" in line 26?

Q6   Look at how the blackbird is described in lines 31-36.

How do you think the narrator feels about the bird at the end of the poem?

Extension activity

- The poet's brother died in an accident when he was young. What evidence can you find in the poem to suggest that the narrator may be the poet himself?

Other poems include similar themes...
Sadness: 'The Wild Swans at Coole', p.6, 'A Vision', p.20; Memory: 'Crossing the Loch', p.30, 'Cold Knap Lake', p.24; Family Relationships: 'Price We Pay for the Sun', p.26.

Simon Armitage

Simon Armitage was born in 1963 in West Yorkshire. As well as poetry,
he's also written four stage plays, and writes for TV, film and radio.

A Vision

The future was a beautiful place, once.
Remember the full-blown balsa-wood town
on public display in the Civic Hall?
The ring-bound sketches, artists' impressions,

5   blueprints of smoked glass and tubular steel,
board-game suburbs, modes of transportation
like fairground rides or executive toys.
Cities like *dreams*, cantilevered by light.

And people like us at the bottle-bank
10   next to the cycle-path, or dog-walking
over tended strips of fuzzy-felt grass,
or model drivers, motoring home in

electric cars. Or after the late show –
strolling the boulevard. They were the plans,
15   all underwritten in the neat left-hand
of architects – a true, legible script.

I pulled that future out of the north wind
at the landfill site, stamped with today's date,
riding the air with other such futures,
20   all unlived in and now fully extinct.

POEM DICTIONARY
balsa-wood — lightweight wood used for model making
cantilevered — supported
boulevard — a wide, open street
underwritten — signed
legible — neat, easily read

A Vision

Q1   Look at the poem's title.

    a)   What does "A Vision" make you think of? Does it sound positive or negative?

    b)   Why do you think Armitage chose this title?

Q2   Choose three images the narrator uses to describe the future town in lines 2-14.

    a)   For each image, explain its effect.

    b)   How do you think he feels about the plans for the future overall?

Q3   Look carefully at the language in line 1.

Why do you think the narrator says "was" and "once"?

The future of urban transportation.

Q4   How do think the narrator feels about the town's planners and architects?
Explain your answer using quotes from the poem.

Q5   Compare lines 1 and 20. Why do you think Armitage uses these two lines to open and close his poem?

Extension activities

- What would your ideal future town be like? Write down some suggestions for it.
- Do you think it's possible to build a town like the one you've described? What could you do to make sure the plans were carried out more successfully than the ones in the poem?

Other poems touch on these themes...
Bitterness and anger: 'London', p.4, 'Neighbours', p.28; Urban Life: 'Hard Water', p.32.

Margaret Atwood

<u>Margaret Atwood</u> was born in 1939 in Ontario, Canada. She graduated in 1961 from the University of Toronto, and has since taught at various Canadian universities as well as writing professionally, receiving numerous awards for both her poetry and works of fiction.

The Moment

The moment when, after many years
of hard work and a long voyage
you stand in the centre of your room,
house, half-acre, square mile, island, country,
5   knowing at last how you got there,
and say, _I own this_,

is the same moment when the trees unloose
their soft arms from around you,
the birds take back their language,
10   the cliffs fissure and collapse,
the air moves back from you like a wave
and you can't breathe.

_No_, they whisper. _You own nothing._
You were a visitor, time after time
15   _climbing the hill, planting the flag, proclaiming._
We never belonged to you.
You never found us.
It was always the other way round.

The birds came to take
back their language.

<u>POEM DICTIONARY</u>
voyage — long journey
fissure — split
proclaiming — announcing

The Moment

Q1   What impression do you get of the person the poet describes in the first stanza?

Q2   How does the tone change in the second stanza?

Q3   Look at the language in the second stanza.

Copy and complete the table below using two words or phrases that you find effective. For each one, explain why.

Here's one to start you off. →

Word or phrase	Reason for effectiveness
"unloose"	gentle sounding, but unsettling

Q4   What is the mood in the final stanza? How has this been created?

Q5   Do you think the order of the stanzas in this poem is important? Explain your answer.

Q6   Why do you think the poet has chosen not to use a rhyme scheme in this poem?

Q7   What do you think the overall message of this poem is?

Extension activity
- What do you think might have inspired Margaret Atwood to write this poem?

Compare the themes in this poem with...
The Power of Nature: 'Storm in the Black Forest', p.14, 'Spellbound', p.10;
Nature vs Mankind: 'The Prelude', p.8, 'Below the Green Corrie', p.12, 'Wind', p.16.

Gillian Clarke

<u>Gillian Clarke</u> was born in 1937 in Cardiff. She teaches creative writing at the University of Glamorgan. Many of her poems reflect her cultural identity and family relationships in Wales.

Cold Knap Lake

We once watched a crowd
pull a drowned child from the lake.
Blue-lipped and dressed in water's long green silk
she lay for dead.

5   Then kneeling on the earth,
a heroine, her red head bowed,
her wartime cotton frock soaked,
my mother gave a stranger's child her breath.
The crowd stood silent,
10   drawn by the dread of it.

The child breathed, bleating
and rosy in my mother's hands.
My father took her home to a poor house
and watched her thrashed for almost drowning.

15   Was I there?
Or is that troubled surface something else
shadowy under the dipped fingers of willows
where satiny mud blooms in cloudiness
after the treading, heavy webs of swans
20   as their wings beat and whistle on the air?

All lost things lie under closing water
in that lake with the poor man's daughter.

<u>POEM DICTIONARY</u>
satiny — smooth, glossy (like satin)

Cold Knap Lake

Q1   Summarise the events the narrator describes in the first two stanzas.

Q2   Does the narrator sound certain or uncertain
      about what happened in the first three stanzas?

Q3   Look at line 15.

   a)   What effect does this line have on the poem's tone and content?

   b)   What effect does it have on the reader?

Q4   How does the narrator present her memories in the fourth stanza?

Q5   The poet chooses to end the poem with a rhyming couplet.

   a)   Why do you think she does this? Is it important?

   b)   What do you think these final two lines mean?

**Meet Jen and Ben.
They're a rhyming couplet.**

Extension activity

- Imagine the poet's mum was telling the same story. Do you think her memory of the event
  would be different to her daughter's? Would it be any more reliable? Explain your answers.

Other poems touch on these themes...

Memory: 'Crossing the Loch', p.30, 'The Wild Swans at Coole', p.6,
'The Blackbird of Glanmore', p.18; Uncertainty: 'The Prelude', p.8.

Grace Nichols

Grace Nichols was born in Guyana in 1950. She was a teacher and journalist in the Caribbean until she moved to Britain in 1977. Both of these cultures and how they interlink are important to her.

Price We Pay for the Sun

These islands
not picture postcards
for unravelling tourist
you know
5   these islands real
more real
than flesh and blood
past stone
past foam
10 these islands split
bone

my mother's breasts
like sleeping volcanoes
who know
15 what kinda sulph-furious
cancer tricking her
below
while the wind
constantly whipping
20 my father's tears
to salty hurricanes
and my grandmother's croon
sifting sand
water mirroring palm

25 Poverty is the price
we pay for the sun girl
run come

POEM DICTIONARY
croon — sing softly / soothingly

Section Two — Contemporary Poems

Price We Pay for the Sun

Q1   How would you describe the narrator's tone in the opening four lines of the poem?

Q2   What do you think the poet means by the phrase "unravelling tourist"?

> The Caribbean dialect is a variation of the English language. It uses different words and sentence constructions to Standard English.

Q3   Nichols has written this poem in a mixture of Standard English and Caribbean dialect.

   a)   Find three examples of dialect words or phrases.

   b)   What effect does writing in dialect have in this poem?

Q4   Choose an image from each of the first two stanzas.

For each one, explain what you think it says about the narrator's feelings towards the islands.

Q5   A student writes, "The narrator has conflicting feelings towards the islands."

Do you agree with this statement? Why / why not?
Support your answer with evidence from the poem.

Q6   Suggest two possible meanings for the poem's title.

Extension activity
- Find some images of Caribbean islands. Look at the pictures together with the poem.
  Do the pictures help you understand the poem better? If so, how?

Compare the themes in this poem with...
<u>Home:</u> 'Hard Water', p.32; <u>Relationships:</u> 'The Blackbird of Glanmore', p.18;
<u>The Power of Nature:</u> 'The Prelude', p.8, 'Wind', p.16, 'Storm in the Black Forest', p.14.

Gillian Clarke

<u>Gillian Clarke</u> was born in 1937 in Cardiff. She teaches creative writing at the University of Glamorgan. Many of her poems reflect her cultural identity and family relationships in Wales.

Neighbours

That spring was late. We watched the sky
and studied charts for shouldering isobars.
Birds were late to pair. Crows drank from the lamb's eye.

Over Finland small birds fell: song-thrushes
5   steering north, smudged signatures on light,
migrating warblers, nightingales.

Wing-beats failed over fjords, each lung a sip of gall.
Children were warned of their dangerous beauty.
Milk was spilt in Poland. Each quarrel

10   the blowback from some old story,
a mouthful of bitter air from the Ukraine
brought by the wind out of its box of sorrows.

This spring a lamb sips caesium on a Welsh hill.
A child, lifting her head to drink the rain,
15   takes into her blood the poisoned arrow.

Now we are all neighbourly, each little town
in Europe twinned to Chernobyl, each heart
with the burnt firemen, the child on the Moscow train.

In the democracy of the virus and the toxin
20   we wait. We watch for spring migrations,
one bird returning with green in its voice.

Glasnost. Golau glas. A first break of blue.

<u>POEM DICTIONARY</u>
isobar — line on a weather map
fjords — long, thin, coastal valleys filled by the sea
gall — something bitter
Ukraine — Eastern European country, under Communist rule until 1991
caesium — a radioactive (and poisonous) element
Chernobyl — a city in the Ukraine. A nuclear power plant exploded there in 1986.
Glasnost — a government policy in the Ukraine which encouraged honesty and openness
Golau glas — Welsh for 'blue light'

Neighbours

Q1 a) How does the poet set the scene in the first two stanzas?

    b) What sort of mood does she create in the first stanza?

Q2 How does Clarke present the effects of Chernobyl in stanzas 3 and 4?

Hint: think about her language, the images
she uses and any features of form.

Q3 Choose two images that show how the disaster is still affecting people in the present day. Explain the effect of these images.

Q4 How do you think the narrator feels in this poem? Choose one or more of the following words and explain your answer using quotes from the poem.

| afraid | angry | bitter | sad | hopeful |

Q5 The final line of the poem is set apart from the rest.

Why do you think the poet has done this?

Extension activity

* Find some news reports or information about the Chernobyl disaster.
  Do you think the poet has presented the after-effects well? Explain your answer.

Compare the themes in this poem with...

Anger and Bitterness: 'London', p.4, 'A Vision', p.20; Hope for the Future: 'London', p.4, 'A Vision', p.20, 'Wind', p.16; Relationships: 'The Blackbird of Glanmore', p.18.

Kathleen Jamie

Kathleen Jamie is a Scottish poet, born in Edinburgh in 1962, now living in Fife. She studied at the University of Edinburgh and has since been 'writer-in-residence' at different universities. She has won several awards for her poetry since receiving the Creative Scotland award in 2001.

Crossing the Loch

Remember how we rowed toward the cottage
on the sickle-shaped bay,
that one night after the pub
loosed us through its swinging doors
5   and we pushed across the shingle
till water lipped the sides
as though the loch mouthed 'boat'?

I forget who rowed. Our jokes hushed.
The oars' splash, creak, and the spill
10   of the loch reached long into the night.
Out in the race I was scared:
the cold shawl of breeze,
and hunched hills; what the water held
of deadheads, ticking nuclear hulls.

15   Who rowed, and who kept their peace?
Who hauled salt-air and stars
deep into their lungs, were not reassured;
and who first noticed the loch's
phosphorescence, so, like a twittering nest
20   washed from the rushes, an astonished
small boat of saints, we watched water shine
on our fingers and oars,
the magic dart of our bow wave?

It was surely foolhardy, such a broad loch, a tide,
25   but we live – and even have children
to women and men we had yet to meet
that night we set out, calling our own
the sky and salt-water, wounded hills
dark-starred by blaeberries, the glimmering anklets
30   we wore in the shallows
as we shipped oars and jumped,
to draw the boat safe, high at the cottage shore.

POEM DICTIONARY
loch — Scottish lake
sickle-shaped — curved
shingle — gravel
deadheads — logs sunk in water
phosphorescence — glow of light
blaeberries — Scottish word for blackberries

Crossing the Loch

Q1   a)   Who do you think the narrator is talking to in this poem?

      b)   What effect does the narrator's use of words like "we" and "us" have on the reader?

Q2   Pick out an image from each stanza that you think best sums up the mood at that point. Copy out the table below and fill it in using the images you've chosen. Explain the effect of each image.

Here's one to start you off.

Image	Mood	Effect
"the pub / loosed us"	happy	Sounds relaxed and carefree

Q3   What is your overall impression of the loch itself?

Q4   The narrator asks several questions, e.g. "Who rowed, and who kept their peace?" What is the effect of these questions?

Q5   Why do you think the poet wrote this poem?

Extension activity

- Describe an event that's special to you from when you were younger. Think carefully about how you felt at the time. Why is this event so important to you? Which bits really stand out in your mind? Which details have you forgotten?

Other poems touch on these themes...

Memory: Cold Knap Lake, p.24, 'The Blackbird of Glanmore', p.18; Special Places: 'The Wild Swans at Coole', p.6, 'Below the Green Corrie', p.12 ; The Magic of Nature: 'Spellbound', p.10.

Jean Sprackland

<u>Jean Sprackland</u> was born in Burton upon Trent, in the Midlands, in 1962, but now lives in Southport in Merseyside. Burton is famous for its breweries, which use the local water to brew the beer.

Hard Water

I tried the soft stuff on holiday in Wales,
a mania of teadrinking and hairwashing,
excitable soap which never rinsed away,

but I loved coming home to this.
5   Flat. Straight. Like the vowels,
like the straight talk: *hey up me duck*.
I'd run the tap with its swimming-pool smell,
get it cold and anaesthetic. Stand the glass
and let the little fizz of anxiety settle.
10 Honest water, bright and not quite clean.
The frankness of limestone, of gypsum,
the sour steam of cooling towers,
the alchemical taste of brewing.

On pitiless nights, I had to go for the bus
15 before last orders. I'd turn up my face,
let rain scald my eyelids and lips.
It couldn't lie. Fell thick
with a payload of acid. No salt –
this rain had forgotten the sea.
20 I opened my mouth, speaking nothing
in spite of my book-learning.
I let a different cleverness wash my tongue.
It tasted of work, the true taste
of early mornings, the blunt taste
25 of *don't get mardy*, of *too bloody deep for me*,
fierce lovely water that marked me for life
as belonging, regardless.

<u>POEM DICTIONARY</u>
hard water — water containing limestone, characteristic of the Midlands
gypsum — a mineral
alchemical — changing things that aren't worth anything into something valuable
mardy — grumpy, sulky (midlands dialect)

Hard Water

Q1 How do Sprackland's descriptions of the Welsh water on holiday contrast with her descriptions of the hard water back home?

Q2 The poet links hard water to the qualities she admires in the local people, e.g. "like the straight talk". Make a list of some of the words and phrases she uses to do this.

Q3 What impression do you get of the poet's home town? Use quotes to support your answer.

Q4 Look at the final two lines of the poem.

   a) What do you think the poet means by these lines?

   b) How do these ideas fit in with the rest of the poem?

English parties often turn into a mania of teadrinking.

Q5 Hard water could be seen as an unusual subject for a poem. Why do you think the poet chose to write about it?

Extension activity

- Imagine you were going to write a poem about your home town. Make a list of everything you associate with it. Which of the items on your list do you think sum up the characteristics of the town best? Which ones would you write about in your poem?

Several poems contain these themes...

Important Places: 'Price We Pay for the Sun', p.26, 'The Blackbird of Glanmore', p.18.

The Urban Environment: 'London', p.4, 'A Vision', p.20.

Place

Q1   Look at the poems in this cluster.

     a)   Name five different types of place.

     b)   Name five different feelings associated with these places.

Q2   Think about your favourite place.

     a)   Write a brief description of this place. What makes it so special? How does it make you feel?

     b)   Which poem relates most closely to your feelings about your favourite place? Explain your answer.

Q3   a)   For each of the feelings below, choose a poem from the cluster that you think matches it best. Support your answer with a quotation from the poem.

         E.g. Sadness — 'The Blackbird of Glanmore' — "I think of one gone to him".

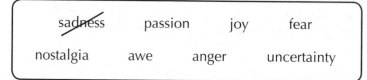

~~sadness~~	passion	joy	fear
nostalgia	awe	anger	uncertainty

     b)   Pick one of the poems you chose in part a).
           Write down at least two other feelings you associate with it.

     c)   Do any of the feelings in this poem contradict each other or are they all consistent? Can you explain why this is?

Place

Q4 Some poets link an event with the place where it happens.

Choose two poems where the events described are linked with a specific place. Copy and complete the table below to compare how these events are shown.

	Poem 1	Poem 2
Place		
Event		
Form and structure		
Language and imagery		

Q5 Choose a poem that presents a positive attitude towards a place.

a) How does the poet's language reflect this?

b) What are the feelings and attitudes in this poem?

Q6 Choose a poem that presents a negative attitude towards a place.

How do the feelings and attitudes in this poem compare to those in the poem you chose for Q5?

Exam-Style Questions

Remember to make a proper plan before you start writing out your answer.

|0|7| Compare how places are presented in *Crossing the Loch* and **one** other poem from 'Place'.

(36 marks)

|0|8| Compare how a place is shown in *Hard Water* and **one** other poem from 'Place'.

(36 marks)

36

Nature

Q1   a)   List the poems in this cluster that are about nature in some way.

     b)   Why do you think so many poets choose to write about nature?

Q2   Link these images of nature with the poems they come from.

"Winds stampeding the fields"	'Below the Green Corrie'
"The giant trees are bending"	'The Prelude'
"mountains gathered round me / like bandits"	'Spellbound'
"cliffs fissure and collapse"	'Wind'
"a huge peak, black and huge"	'The Moment'

Q3   a)   List five different feelings towards nature that are presented in the poems.

     b)   What do you think the most common feeling is?
Explain your answer by referring to at least three of the poems.

Q4   Choose one poem from the Literary Heritage and one contemporary poem. Compare how the two poems present nature by copying and completing the table below.

	Poem 1	Poem 2
Form and structure		
Language		
Feelings and attitudes		

Nature

Q5   Choose a poem you think is about the relationship between humans and nature.

What do you think the poem has to say about this relationship?
Support your answer with quotations.

Who says man and
nature can't be friends?

Q6   Choose a poem you think is about the power of nature.

a)   How does the form support this theme?

b)   What language does the poet use to describe nature?

c)   What are the feelings and attitudes presented in this poem?

Q7   Choose two other poems about nature from this cluster.

a)   What aspect of nature do they present?

b)   How do they do this? Think about form, structure and language.

c)   Which poem do you prefer? Why?

Exam-Style Questions

| 0 | 3 | Compare how nature is presented in *Storm in the Black Forest* and **one** other
poem from 'Place'.   *(36 marks)*

| 0 | 4 | Compare how nature is shown in *Below the Green Corrie* and **one** other poem
from 'Place'.   *(36 marks)*

Memory

Q1   Choose a poem from the 'Place' cluster that includes:

a)   a happy memory

b)   a sad or painful memory

Support each of your answers with a quote from the poem.

Joanne definitely had
somewhere to be, she just
couldn't remember where...

Q2   a)   Make a list of the feelings associated with memory in 'The Wild Swans at Coole'.

b)   Make a list of the feelings associated with memory in another poem from the cluster. How similar are your two lists?

Q3   Choose two poems that suggest memories are not always reliable.

Compare how the two poets use language to suggest memories can be unreliable.

Q4   Choose a poem that you think presents memory in a positive way.

a)   What is the narrator remembering in this poem?

b)   How does the poet present positive feelings about this memory?

Q5   In these poems, memories are often strongly linked with place.

a)   Choose a poem that you think presents memories that are triggered by a particular place. How does the poet present the link between memories and place?

b)   How do the ideas about memory in this poem compare with those in the one you chose for Q4?

Sadness

Q1   a)   Choose two poems from this cluster that you think are sad.

     b)   What is the narrator sad about in each poem?

     c)   Are the feelings of sadness in either of these poems
          similar to anything you've experienced? How?

Q2   a)   Use a thesaurus to look up five different words for "sad".

     b)   Which poems could these words apply to?

Q3   Pick two other poems that you think are sad.
     These should be different to the ones you picked for Q1.

     a)   Compare how the language used in each poem expresses a feeling
          of sadness. Support your answer with quotes from the poems.

     b)   Compare how the form of each poem adds to the feeling of sadness.
          Explain your answer.

Exam-Style Questions

[0][4]   Compare how memories are presented in *The Wild Swans at Coole* and **one**
         other poem from 'Place'.   *(36 marks)*

[0][5]   Compare how a feeling of sadness is presented in *Neighbours* and **one** other
         poem from 'Place'.   *(36 marks)*

Uncertainty

Q1　a)　Make a list of the poems in this cluster that you think are about uncertainty.

　　b)　What are the characters in these poems uncertain about?
　　　　The list below should give you a few ideas.

> the future　　memories　　feelings　　the world around them

Q2　a)　Describe a time when you felt uncertain about something.

　　b)　Does this help you to empathise with any of the characters in the poems?
　　　　Explain your answer.

Q3　Choose a poem from your answer to Q1.

　　a)　How does the poem's language suggest uncertainty?

　　b)　How does the poem's form add to the sense of uncertainty?

Q4　Choose a poem where the narrator or characters are certain of themselves.

　　a)　What are the feelings and attitudes in this poem?

　　b)　How does the language compare to the poem you picked for Q3?

Relationships

Q1   Choose a poem from this cluster that's about:

a)   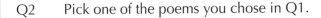 a happy or loving relationship

b)   a confusing or painful relationship

"It's so over between us..."
"Yes dear."

Q2   Pick one of the poems you chose in Q1.

How is the relationship presented?
Think about form, structure and language.

Q3   Can you relate to any of the feelings about relationships described in these poems?
Explain your answer.

Q4   Choose a poem about a relationship that is linked to a place.

a)   What kind of relationship is described in this poem?

b)   What are the feelings and attitudes in this relationship?

c)   How are the relationship and the place linked together?

Exam-Style Questions

| 0 | 5 | Compare how feelings of uncertainty are shown in *The Prelude* and **one** other
poem from 'Place'.   *(36 marks)*

| 0 | 6 | Compare how relationships are presented in *The Blackbird of Glanmore* and
one other poem from 'Place'.   *(36 marks)*

Passion

Q1   Being passionate means having intense feelings about something.
Choose a poem from the cluster where the narrator is passionate about:

a)   a place

b)   nature

Q2   Match these passionate phrases to the poems they come from:

"jugfull after jugfull of pure white liquid fire"	'Wind'
"mind-forged manacles"	'Hard Water'
"the stones cry out under the horizons"	'Spellbound'
"I cannot, cannot go"	'Storm in the Black Forest'
"fierce lovely water that marked me for life"	'London'

Q3   Choose a poem that you consider to be passionate.

a)   What are the feelings and attitudes in this poem? Are they all positive ones?

b)   How does the language used in the poem show a sense of passion?

Q4   Choose two poems that are passionate about a place.
Copy and complete the table below with notes about the poems.

	Poem 1	Poem 2
Form and structure		
Language		
Feelings and ideas		

Hope

Q1   Name a time when you've hoped for something. Did you get what you hoped for?

Q2   a)   Which of the poems in the 'Place' cluster do you think are hopeful?
            Name at least two.

      b)   Give an example of hopeful language for each of the poems you chose in part a).

Q3   a)   Which of the poems in this cluster do you think are lacking in hope?
            Name at least three.

      b)   Choose two of the poems you picked for part a).
            Compare how this lack of hope is presented.

Q4   Look back at the poems you chose for Q3 part b).

      How do you respond to these poems? Do you agree with
      the feelings and attitudes in them? Explain your answer.

Exam-Style Questions

0 5   Compare how intense feelings are presented in _London_ and **one** other poem
       from 'Place'.   _(36 marks)_

0 6   Compare how hope is shown in _Neighbours_ and **one** other poem from 'Place'.
                                                                      (36 marks)

Mark Scheme

This section is a bit <u>different</u> — it's your chance to get inside the <u>examiner's mind</u>.

1) The mark scheme below is <u>very similar</u> to the one that the <u>examiners will use</u> to mark your actual exam answers.

2) The point of this section is to show you exactly what the examiners are <u>looking for</u> and <u>what you'll need to do</u> on the day to get high marks.

3) You have to <u>read</u> the <u>sample extracts</u> of exam answers. Then you'll either mark the answer and say how it can be improved, or add some extra points to make the answer better. The mark scheme will help you do this.

4) Before you start grading the sample answers, make sure you've read the mark scheme really <u>thoroughly</u> and that you <u>understand everything</u>.

Grade	What you've written
A*	• Explores several interpretations or meanings in detail • Provides carefully chosen and well-integrated quotes to back up ideas • Compares the poems thoughtfully and in detail, using plenty of evidence • Looks closely at <u>how</u> language, form and structure affect the reader with well-chosen examples • Gives detailed and imaginative ideas about themes, attitudes and feelings • Considers the evidence to come up with conclusions about the poem
A	• Gives several interpretations or meanings • Provides well-chosen quotes to support ideas • Compares the poems in detail and provides plenty of evidence • Describes <u>how</u> language, form and structure affect the reader, using examples • Looks at themes, attitudes and feelings in detail, again using plenty of evidence
B	• Thoughtful interpretation of the poems • Supports interpretations with quotes from the text • Provides some well-chosen evidence to support comparisons between the poems • Gives several examples of <u>how</u> language, form and structure affect the reader • Provides some evidence to support ideas about themes, attitudes and feelings
C	• Comments on several aspects of the poem, e.g. mood, language, feelings, and uses quotes to back the comments up • Makes several comparisons between the poems • Explains <u>how</u> language, form and structure affect the reader • Makes valid comments about themes, attitudes or feelings in the poems

You'll also be marked on your <u>spelling</u>, <u>punctuation</u> and <u>grammar</u> and on how you <u>present</u> your work. To get the <u>best marks</u>, your essay should be <u>clearly organised</u> into <u>well-structured</u> paragraphs. It should also be <u>easy</u> to follow and <u>understand</u>.

Adding Quotes and Developing Points

The sample answers on this page have just one thing missing. Your task is to improve each point by adding a quote from the poem which backs it up. Good luck...

> | 0 | 1 | Compare how ideas about places are presented in
> *Hard Water* and one other poem from 'Place'.
> *(36 marks)*

Answer Extract 1

In this sample answer, some sentences have letters like this: **(A)**.
Replace each letter with a suitable quote to help the student get a better grade.

Both 'Hard Water' and 'Spellbound' are poems which explore the idea of a place being important to people. In 'Hard Water', we are told about the specific place which is important, whilst in 'Spellbound', it is much less clear where the poem is set.

Both poets describe a strong tie to the places that they are writing about, but in different ways. For Sprackland, the taste of the water strengthens her connection to the area where she grew up. She suggests her home town is a place that makes her feel safe and comfortable when she says: **(A)**. Brontë, on the other hand, talks about being spellbound by the place she is in. The magic of the storm is holding her captive and she is unable to leave. Unlike Sprackland, she makes the place she describes seem both exciting and frightening with descriptions such as: **(B)**.

Answer Extract 2

In this sample answer, some sentences have letters like this: **(A)**.
Replace each letter with a suitable quote to help the student get a better grade.

Both poets seem to feel bound to the places in their poems. Sprackland talks about "belonging" there "regardless" and appears comforted by this. Her use of dialect phrases such as **(A)** show us how proud she is of the place she is from. Using them is a celebration of the local culture and gives us a real sense of the town and the people who live there. Although Brontë writes about a place that is less personal to her, she also feels a strong pull towards it. Repetition of phrases such as **(B)** emphasise her reluctance to leave.

Adding Quotes and Developing Points

One more extract and two more tasks on this page — develop the points and finish the plan.

| 0 | 1 | Compare how ideas about places are presented in *Hard Water* and one other poem from 'Place'. | (36 marks) |

Answer Extract 3

In this sample answer, some sentences have letters like this: **(A)**. These points need to be developed further. Write an extra sentence or two to develop each point.

> Both poets use some unusual or surprising language to describe the places they are writing about. Some of Sprackland's descriptions of her home town seem quite negative at first, for example "sour steam of cooling towers" and "pitiless nights". They make the area sound harsh and industrial. It seems unusual that she chooses to describe the place in this way. **(A)**
>
> Brontë also describes the place she is in using negative terms. She makes the storm appear dark and threatening when she says things like "Wastes beyond wastes below". But in the last line she suggests that she actually wants to stay, despite the danger, when she says "I will not, cannot go". **(B)**

| 0 | 2 | Compare the ways in which ideas about place are presented in *The Wild Swans at Coole* and one other poem from 'Place'. | (36 marks) |

Sample Plan

The table below is a plan for an answer to the question above.

Find a quotation from the poem to back up each of the language points in the table. Make brief notes on your personal response to each poem to complete the plan.

	The Wild Swans at Coole	**Below the Green Corrie**
Themes and Ideas	Change and the passing of time, the beauty of nature	Nature is seen as both a threat and a positive thing
Language	Of beauty / admiration ... **(A)** Of time ... **(B)**	Bandit imagery ... **(C)**
Form and Structure	First person narration — shows narrator's private thoughts	First person narration — shows strong emotions
Personal Response	**(D)**	**(E)**

Marking Answer Extracts

This page is all about marking sample exam answers. If you're reading this without having read the mark scheme on p.44 first — do not collect £200 and certainly DO NOT pass GO.

> | 0 | 3 | Compare how feelings towards nature are presented in
> *Storm in the Black Forest* and one other poem from 'Place'. *(36 marks)*

Answer Extract 4

1) Use the mark scheme on p.44 to <u>mark</u> this extract.
2) <u>Explain</u> how you decided on the grade and say how the answer could be <u>improved</u>.

> In 'Storm in the Black Forest', the poet is describing a lightning storm. He brings it to life in the mind of the reader when he describes the lightning as "pure white liquid fire" and the sound of the thunder as "uncouth sounds". This is similar to 'Wind' where Hughes describes "Winds stampeding the fields under the window" and "the brunt wind that dented the balls of my eyes". In both of these poems, the reader can relate the descriptions to their own experience because of the way in which the poets have made the weather seem real. Both of the poems emphasise the power of the weather through the choice of language made by the poets.

This first extract has been <u>marked for you</u> to show you what to do.

Response: This answer gets a grade | C | because it comments on one of the poems' main themes and explains how some of the language affects the reader. It also provides examples of this. To get a grade B, it needs to make more specific comments about the language and go into more detail about the effects of the quoted lines.

Answer Extract 5

1) Use the mark scheme to <u>mark</u> this extract from a sample answer to the question above.
2) <u>Explain</u> how you decided on the grade and say how the answer could be <u>improved</u>.

> Both 'Storm in the Black Forest' and 'Wind' are poems about the power of nature and how dramatic weather can be. In 'Storm in the Black Forest', the poet vividly describes a night-time thunderstorm using metaphors such as "pure white liquid fire" and "electric liquid" to convey the drama and power of the lightning. The poet's language celebrates the storm's power — the fact that he has named his poem after this event supports this idea. I think that the same is true of 'Wind', where the poet again seems to be celebrating the weather. Hughes gives us some vivid descriptions of the weather such as "the skyline a grimace" and "Winds stampeding". These suggest that the weather is dramatic and violent, and explain why "we grip / Our hearts and cannot entertain book" — the people listening to the wind are so frightened by what they can hear that they cannot think about anything else.

Marking Answer Extracts

Here's the exam question again and an extract from a sample answer to it.

0	3	Compare how feelings towards nature are presented in *Storm in the Black Forest* and one other poem from 'Place'.

(36 marks)

Answer Extract 6

1) Use the mark scheme on p.44 to <u>mark</u> this extract.
2) <u>Explain</u> how you decided on the grade and say how the answer could be <u>improved</u>.

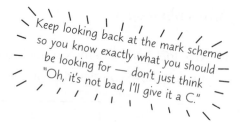
Keep looking back at the mark scheme so you know exactly what you should be looking for — don't just think "Oh, it's not bad, I'll give it a C."

> Both 'Storm in the Black Forest' and 'Wind' are poems which not only describe weather and nature, but also seem to celebrate it. Although set in different places, they both convey the power of a storm through the language they have chosen.
>
> Both poems are about storms which take place at night, which makes the weather appear more frightening. Readers can relate to this because most people have been woken up by the sound of a storm "crashing through darkness", or making the "heavens cackle with uncouth sounds". These onomatopoeic descriptions allow the reader to experience the noise of the storm along with the poet. Lawrence also uses vivid metaphors — describing the lightning as "electric liquid" and a "white snake" — to bring the power of the storm clearly to life and help the reader to visualise events. Hughes similarly describes the skyline as "a grimace" which shows how strong and feared the weather is.
>
> The two poems are not just about impressive storms however. Both poets use language to convey the relative powerlessness of human beings against nature. Lawrence sounds mocking and scornful when he says "This is the electricity that man is supposed to have mastered"; in the final line he repeats "supposed to" to emphasise his point that nature is more powerful than we are. His tone is so convincing, we are forced to agree with him. In 'Wind', Hughes makes the people in the poem sound vulnerable and afraid in the face of the storm when he says that "we grip / Our hearts and cannot entertain book".

Marking Answer Extracts

OK, here's a different sample answer. Hopefully you're getting into the examiner's mind-set by now...

| 0 | 2 | Compare the ways in which ideas about place are presented in *The Wild Swans at Coole* and one other poem from 'Place'. *(36 marks)* |

Answer Extract 7

1) Use the mark scheme on p.44 to <u>mark</u> this extract.

2) <u>Explain</u> how you decided on the grade and say how the answer could be <u>improved</u>.

Don't forget to keep looking back at the mark scheme.

> The 'Wild Swans at Coole' and 'Below the Green Corrie' describe specific places and the impact that these have had on the poets, although their responses are very different.
>
> In the first poem, Yeats describes a place that has had a significant effect on him. We can sense this through the language that he uses in the poem. For example he says that "The trees are in their autumn beauty", which implies that this is a place he loves and admires. MacCaig, on the other hand, suggests that although the place has had a similarly significant impact on him, it is a more negative one. His description of how "The mountains gathered round me / like bandits" gives the impression that he is frightened of the place which "swaggered up close". However, like Yeats, his language celebrates the place he is in with his description of "marvellous prowlers" which seem to have "enriched" his life. This suggests that he is somewhat confused about his relationship with this place — he does not know whether he loves it or hates it. Yeats, on the other hand, does not waver from the fact that he loves this place and the "Mysterious, beautiful" swans that he sees there.

50

Marking a Complete Answer

New page, new question and answer. Only this time it's the whole answer, not just an extract...

---

0 4   Compare how places are presented in *The Prelude* and one other poem from 'Place'.

(36 marks)

Answer 8

Make sure you've <u>read</u> the <u>advice</u> and <u>mark</u> <u>scheme</u> on page 44.

Read the <u>whole</u> answer. Use the mark scheme to <u>mark</u> the answer. <u>Explain</u> how you decided on the grade and say how the answer could be <u>improved</u>.

Both 'The Prelude' and 'Crossing the Loch' are powerful accounts of similar journeys across lakes, although set in very different times and places. Whilst Wordsworth describes a boat journey across a "silent lake" in the Lake District in the 1800s, Jamie takes her reader across a Scottish Loch "long into the night" more than 150 years later. Despite the differences in time and place, both poets convey similar feelings about their journeys.

In both poems, there is a clear sense of celebration both of the journey itself and of the places that they experience. Wordsworth describes how, once he was on the lake, there "Was nothing but the stars and the grey sky" above him which gives the reader a clear sense of the fact that man is insignificant in the face of nature. Jamie takes a similar idea, explaining how she "was scared" of the "hunched hills" which I think again shows us how small people are in comparison to the world. Despite this fear, both poets still choose to write about the events, which I think suggests that they are impressed by the power and scale of nature, as well as being scared of it.

Wordsworth vividly describes the place in his poem, which helps the reader to see what he saw and to really feel that they are experiencing these events with him. He describes the "huge peak, black and huge" and the "Small circles glittering idly in the moon", all of which bring the scene to life. This both celebrates the place and shows his insignificance in comparison. Jamie also brings the scene to life when she describes how "water lipped the sides / as though the loch mouthed 'boat' ". This use of onomatopoeia helps the reader to hear the sound of the water against the side of the boat, which in turn helps us to experience this moonlit crossing with the poet. Like Wordsworth, I feel that the language here is celebratory and reflects the poet's insignificance in the world. When Jamie says that the boaters were "an astonished / small boat of saints", it might suggest that they were worshipping the amazing spectacle that they had just seen.

Section Four — Analysing Answers

Marking a Complete Answer

This is the second half of the answer on p.50.

In both poems, the poets' use of form and structure help to make their description of events and places come to life. Wordsworth writes a dramatic monologue which suggests to the reader that this is both a real event and a significant one. In fact, this "act of stealth / And troubled pleasure" became far more to him than a simple boat ride on a lake. We know that this event stayed with him long after it happened because he describes how "for many days" he couldn't see or write clearly because he "had seen / That spectacle" and that his memories of the mountain "were a trouble" to his dreams. This links with the idea of man's insignificance.

Jamie's poem also seems to be a reminiscence. Her memory starts in the first stanza, using the first person as if she is talking to someone who was there with her: "Remember how we....". This suggests that she has a sense of pride in the event because she obviously wants to talk about it. Each stanza of the poem moves the boat across the loch: the first is the decision to take the boat out "one night after the pub"; she then moves on to describe how, once on the water, "I was scared" which suggests that the plan was not well thought out because "Our jokes hushed". This may suggest that it was only then that they realised that "what the water held" might be dangerous. The third stanza puts us with them on the loch admiring the place. They seem to have forgotten to be scared and are, instead, impressed by "the magic dart of our bow wave". The final stanza shows us how Jamie sees the event now, as something "foolhardy" but there is no sense of regret. She seems to still be proud of what they did, and the final line "safe, high at the cottage shore" is her way of saying that they took a risk and survived, and that is something to be proud of.

In both cases, the poets have made their feelings about the places that they describe feel real through their choices of words and the ways in which they describe them. With Wordsworth we can see how "the grim shape / Towered up between me and the stars" and feel the power of the natural world; with Jamie we can feel "the cold shawl of breeze" and the fear that it brought with it. Both poets convey the sense of awesomeness and magic about the places they visited.

Acknowledgments

The Publisher would like to thank:

Simon Armitage: 'A Vision' — *From Tyrannosaurus Rex Versus the Corduroy Kid* (Faber and Faber, 2007)
Margaret Atwood: 'The Moment' — Reproduced with permission of Curtis Brown Group Ltd. London on behalf of Margaret Atwood Copyright © Margaret Atwood 1998
Gillian Clarke: 'Cold Knap Lake' — From *Collected Poems* (Carcanet Press, 1997), reproduced by permission of Carcanet Press Ltd.
Gillian Clarke: 'Neighbours' — From *Letting in the Rumour* (Carcanet Press, 1989), reproduced by permission of Carcanet Press Ltd.
Seamus Heaney: 'The Blackbird of Glanmore' — From *District and Circle* (Faber and Faber, 2006)
Ted Hughes: 'Wind' — From *The Hawk in the Rain*, Faber and Faber; New Impression edition (5 Jun 2003)
Kathleen Jamie: 'Crossing the Loch' — reproduced with permission of Picador, an imprint of Pan Macmillan, London. Copyright © Kathleen Jamie 2002
Norman MacCaig: 'Below the Green Corrie' — from *The Poems of Norman MacCaig* by Norman MacCaig is reproduced by permission of Polygon, an imprint of Birlinn Ltd. (www.birlinn.co.uk)
Grace Nichols: 'Price We Pay for the Sun' — Reproduced with permission of Curtis Brown Group Ltd, London on behalf of Grace Nichols Copyright © Grace Nichols 1984
Jean Sprackland: 'Hard Water' — From *Hard Water* by Jean Sprackland, published by Jonathan Cape. Reprinted by permission of The Random House Group Ltd.
W.B. Yeats: 'The Wild Swans at Coole' — From The *Wild Swans at Coole* (Macmillan and co, 1919), reproduced by permission of AP Watt Ltd. on behalf of Grainne Yeats

Every effort has been made to locate copyright holders and obtain permission to reproduce poems and images. For those poems and images where it has been difficult to trace the originator of the work, we would be grateful for information. If any copyright holder would like us to make an amendment to the acknowledgements, please notify us and we will gladly update the book at the next reprint. Thank you.

APHW41

GCSE English Literature

GCSE
AQA Anthology

Poetry Cluster: Place

For New GCSE courses starting from Sept '10

Answer Book
Higher Level

2

The Answers

Contents

A bullet point (•) before an answer means it's a suggested answer — there are many different possible answers.

Section One

Page 5 — London

Q1. a) ABAB

b) • It makes the poem sound more compelling when read aloud.
• It is very consistent and seems to reinforce the poet's message of relentless misery.

Q2. • "chartered", "mark", "every"
• Repetition emphasises Blake's message that misery is everywhere and affects everyone in the city.

Q3.
•

Image	Effect
"marriage hearse"	Suggests even happy events like marriage are ruined by death and misery
"infant's cry of fear"	Suggests that children are miserable and afraid
"black'ning church"	Not even the church can stop the damage and destruction

Q4. • Blake uses emotive language to shock and sadden the reader. He does this so they will agree how terrible London society was at the time.

Q5. • I think that Blake wrote this poem in the first person because it makes the poem sound more personal and so more convincing.

Q6. • I think he means that the people themselves are partly responsible for the situation they are in. They are trapped by their own thoughts and attitudes as well as by poverty.

Q7. • I think that Blake wrote this poem to draw people's attention to the awful effects of poverty in London. Perhaps he wanted the people in power to realise just how bad it was so they would do something to improve the situation.

Page 7 — The Wild Swans at Coole

Q1. a) • "The nineteenth autumn has come upon me", "And now my heart is

sore", "All's changed"

b) • It gives a sad feeling to the poem because the narrator sounds nostalgic as he looks back over many years.

Q2. a) • **Youth:** "Unwearied still", "Their hearts have not grown old".
• **Love:** "lover by lover, / They paddle", "Companionable streams", "Their hearts have not grown old", "Passion or conquest... / Attend upon them still".
• **Freedom:** "All suddenly mount", "scatter wheeling", "wander where they will", "flown away".
• **Power:** "All suddenly mount", "scatter wheeling", "great broken rings", "clamorous wings", "brilliant creatures", "Passion or conquest".

b) • I think that the narrator loves and admires the swans, but that they also cause him pain. He seems envious of their youth and companionship.

Q3. • The tone is sad and reflective to begin with, but becomes livelier with the arrival of the swans and their "clamorous wings". It becomes sad and thoughtful again in the final stanza as the narrator considers the swans leaving.

Q4. • I think the poet has chosen a good title for the poem because the word "Wild" sums up everything the narrator envies about the swans.

Q5. • I think Yeats decided to set his poem in autumn to create a feeling of things coming to an end. This seems to be how his narrator feels about his own life.

Page 9 — The Prelude

Q1. a) • "A little boat tied to a willow tree", "Proud of his skill", "She was an elfin pinnace"

b) • The line "It was an act of stealth / And troubled pleasure" could indicate that things are about to go wrong.

Q2. a) • "I struck and struck again", "With trembling oars I turned", "in grave / And serious mood"

b) • I think he feels afraid and confused by the mountain's power. He is no longer as confident as he was at the start of the poem.

Q3. a) personification

b) • It brings the mountain to life,

making it seem more real and more threatening.

Q4. • I think blank verse makes the extract sound more serious and convincing than rhyming verse would.

Q5. a) • The sudden change in tone suggests that nature is changeable and surprising.

b) • The narrator's sudden change from confident to completely overawed suggests that man is arrogant and underestimates nature's power.

Page 11 — Spellbound

Q1. a) ABAB

b) • I think the poet might have chosen this rhyme scheme because it makes the poem sound like a spell or a chant. This emphasises the idea that the narrator is enchanted by the storm.

Q2. a) alliteration

b) • It helps emphasise the descriptions of the storm's wildness.

Q3. • "The wild winds coldly blow" and "giant trees are bending" make the storm sound powerful and dramatic. "Clouds beyond clouds" makes the storm sound endless.

Q4 • Examples of repetition include: "I cannot, cannot go", "And yet I cannot go" and "I will not, cannot go". They emphasise the feeling that the narrator is captivated by the storm and unable to leave.

Q5. a) • The narrator seems bound by the storm. She is frightened, but powerless to leave, even though she may want to.

b) • This line introduces the idea that the narrator is staying out in the storm partly through her own choice. She is spellbound, but willingly.

Page 13 — Below the Green Corrie

Q1. • I think of a "Green Corrie" as being a pretty, peaceful place, somewhere in the mountains. I do not imagine many interesting things happening there.

Q2. a) • The atmosphere in the first stanza

The Answers

is tense and a bit frightening. There are lots of menacing images, e.g. "bandits", "swaggered" and "dark light". The mountains sound like they could be dangerous.

b) • The word "But" changes the tone of the poem. The mood is one of relief. Suddenly, the mountains are a lot less scary and the narrator is the one in control.

Q3. • The idea that the mountains stand and deliver, giving up "their money and their lives" is interesting. It sounds clichéd, like something out of a film or maybe a children's game.

Q4. • I think he means that the mountains have had a positive impact on his life. His experience of them has made his life feel more complete.

Q5. • The image of "marvellous prowlers" makes the mountains sound a bit like magnificent wild lions. The use of the word "swashbuckling" makes them sound exciting and heroic, but still slightly dangerous.

Q6. • I think MacCaig has chosen to describe the mountains as bandits because the imagery sums up the two different sides to them. On the one hand, they are dangerous; on the other, they can be fun and exciting.

Page 15 — Storm in the Black Forest

Q1. • The title sounds dramatic, with "Black Forest" allowing us to picture the scenery. The phrase "almost night" in the first line tells us that dusk is falling and adds to the feeling of drama.

Q2.
•

Colour	Effect
"pure white liquid fire"	Sounds bright, almost dazzling — could be a describing lightning. Makes the storm seem intense.
"gold-bronze flutters"	The storm is made to sound rich, like a precious metal. It seems magical and powerful.

Q3. a) enjambment

b) • It makes the poem sound natural and spontaneous, as if the narrator is getting carried away with the excitement of the events he is describing.

Q4. a) • The word "cackle" is onomatopoeic.

b) • I think the poet chose to use onomatopoeia to capture some of the sounds of the storm, in this case the thunder. It gives the reader a real feeling of what it is like to be caught in the middle of it.

Q5. a) • I think the narrator is criticising human beings for thinking they can control something as wild and powerful as nature.

b) • I think the overall message of the

poem is that nature is incredibly powerful and cannot be tamed or controlled. It should be treated with awe and respect.

Page 17 — Wind

Q1. • The phrase makes it sound like the house has been in the middle of a powerful storm, buffeted by strong winds all night. It also makes the house sound lost and isolated.

Q2. a) a metaphor

b) • It suggests that the storm is powerful enough even to affect the hills. It also describes the noise it makes.

Q3. • "Winds stampeding the fields" — makes the storm sound wild and out of control.

• "dented the balls of my eyes" — makes the storm sound violent and painful.

• "The wind flung a magpie away" — the storm sounds angry and powerful. It damages everything in its path.

Q4. • Hughes makes the people seem vulnerable and afraid. They hide away "deep / In chairs" and "grip" their hearts. The word "grip" in particular makes them sound tense and fearful. They seem powerless to do anything against the storm.

Q5. • The title of the poem is neutral and fairly understated. I think it is effective because it makes the storm's power all the more shocking and dramatic when it is described in the poem.

Section Two

Page 19 — The Blackbird of Glanmore

Q1. • "Filling the stillness with life" — this is a happy image which suggests the bird's importance to the narrator. It seems to represent life.

• "Hedge-hop" — the two one-syllable words echo the bird's quick movements. It is easy to picture it hopping about.

Q2. • "A little stillness dancer" — I think this image is effective because it emphasises the narrator's sadness that his brother was once full of life and joy, but is now still.

Q3. a) • The neighbour was suspicious of the blackbird. He seemed to think it was an omen of death.

b) • I don't think the narrator agrees with his neighbour's point of view. He says that he loves the bird and seems to think of it as a symbol of life, not death.

Q4. a) caesura

b) • The poet's use of caesura here marks the change in mood between the happy first stanza and the sadder, more contemplative, middle stanzas. It has the effect of slowing the reader down so we can absorb this change in mood.

Q5. • The word "Clunks" sounds clumsy and helps to break the contemplative mood of the previous stanza, bringing us back to reality.

Q6. • I think the narrator feels affection for the bird. He uses words like "Hedge-hop", which sounds like a familiar, friendly nickname. He appears glad he always sees the blackbird because he repeats the earlier line "On the grass when I arrive".

Page 21 — A Vision

Q1. a) • When I think of "A Vision" I think of something amazing or miraculous, maybe even religious. I think it sounds positive.

b) • I think Armitage was being ironic when he chose this title. He wants to emphasise that the "Vision" the planners had was not amazing or miraculous.

Q2. a) • "smoked glass and tubular steel" — makes the town sound futuristic and exciting.

• "board-game suburbs" — makes the plans and the town sound childish and fake.

• "transportation / like fairground rides" — sounds exciting at first, but also a bit silly and unrealistic.

b) • He thinks that the plans were too far-fetched to ever come true. They were based in fantasy, not reality, which is why they failed.

Q3. • I think the narrator says "was" and "once" because these words contrast with our idea of the future. They make it clear that these ideas are set in the past and are no longer valid. They suggest that the things the narrator is about to describe will never happen.

Q4. • I think that the narrator blames the architects and planners for the failure of the dream. He makes the plans sound vague and unrealistic when he calls them "sketches, artists' impressions". Old superstitions linked left-handed people with the devil. The narrator may be suggesting that the architects were dishonest and possibly deceptive when he writes about "the neat left-hand / of architects".

Q5. • I think Armitage begins and ends with these lines because they sum up the poem's message. "The future" sounds bright and optimistic, but the

The Answers

bleak "now fully extinct" extinguishes all hope that the dreams for the future will ever be realised.

Page 23 — The Moment

Q1. • The person in the first stanza sounds confident and contented. They seem to be someone who has worked hard to get where they are and now they are starting to relax. They might be a bit complacent.

Q2. • The poem suddenly changes in tone when the narrator begins to describe nature's actions. The language becomes unsettling, then violent and frightening.

Q3.
•

Word or phrase	Reason for effectiveness
"fissure and collapse"	sounds powerful and violent
"you can't breathe"	sounds direct, dramatic and frightening

Q4. • The mood in the final stanza is cold, calm and reproachful. Nature is portrayed as quietly powerful with phrases like "No, they whisper". We are left in no doubt that nature is firmly in control and that the foolish, "proclaiming" humans "own nothing".

Q5. • Yes, I think the order of stanzas is important. The poem would be less effective if the reader was not lulled into a false sense of security with the calm of the first stanza, then shocked by the violence of the second.

Q6. • In my opinion the poet has chosen not to use a rhyme scheme to make her poem sound more serious and convincing. The lack of rhyme scheme allows the reader to focus on her message.

Q7. • For me, the overall message of this poem is that human beings can be arrogant about their place in the world and that we should have more respect for nature. Sometimes we take the things it has given us for granted.

Page 25 — Cold Knap Lake

Q1. • The narrator once watched a crowd of people rescue a drowning girl from a lake. Her mother gives the girl mouth to mouth resuscitation while everyone watches. People are afraid the girl might be dead.

Q2. • The narrator sounds confident and certain of events in the first three stanzas.

Q3. a) • Line 15 completely changes the tone and content of the poem. It suddenly goes from telling a simple story about a dramatic incident to questioning the nature and reliability of memories. The tone changes from confident and assured to vague and confused.

b) • The line shocks the reader, because it suggests that none of what we have read so far is true. It might make us start to question our own memories.

Q4. • Her language becomes vague and uncertain; she uses words such as "shadowy" and "cloudiness" to convey the nature of her memories. She uses enjambment (one sentence lasts most of the stanza) to make the narrator sound thoughtful and dreamy.

Q5. a) • The rhyming couplet emphasises the poet's final point. It is the only rhyming couplet of the entire poem and is in a separate stanza. The rhyme brings the poem to a neat conclusion.

b) • I think the poet means that all memories are like her own ones of the drowning girl — confused and unreliable.

Page 27 — Price We Pay for the Sun

Q1. • I would describe the narrator's tone as assertive and defiant. She sounds slightly irritated with the tourists' point of view when she says, "you know".

Q2. • It could be a play on words with "unravelling" meaning unwinding or relaxing, or that the tourists only have a loose grip on reality.

Q3. a) • "These islands / not picture postcards", "these islands real", "who know"

b) • It makes the narrator sound more believable and convincing — as if she knows what she is talking about because she really is from the area. Talking in dialect also makes the narrator sound proud of her culture and heritage.

Q4. • "more real / than flesh and blood" — suggests that the islands are important to the narrator and that her family are connected to them.

• "wind / constantly whipping / my father's tears / to salty hurricanes" — again, links the islands to her family, suggesting their importance to her. It also sounds like the islands are a place of sorrow and hurt for the narrator.

Q5. • Yes, I agree. On the one hand, the narrator seems proud that the islands are not just "picture postcards" — they have an age and history, "past stone". But on the other hand, they are a place of hardship and pain for her.

Q6. • The title could be a reminder of what the tourists pay to go on holiday in the sun. Or it could mean that the price the islanders pay for the sun is poverty.

Page 29 — Neighbours

Q1. a) • The poet sets the scene using a series of fragmented and disturbing images. We know that something is wrong, but we are not sure what.

b) • The mood in the first stanza is dark and unsettling as a result of images such as "Birds were late to pair". The narrator's tone is ominous.

Q2. • By using emotive images of youth, innocence and the natural world — for example, "small birds fell", "Children were warned" — Clarke highlights the terrible effects of the disaster. The images are still quite disconnected, which creates a feeling of the confusion people must have felt watching events unfold at the time.

Q3. • "This spring a lamb sips caesium on a Welsh hill" — shows just how widespread the effects of the disaster have become. It also uses scientific language to emphasise the reality of the situation.

• "Now we are all neighbourly" — this may be ironic, suggesting that we have always been linked, it has just taken the disaster to show us this.

Q4. • I think the narrator feels anger at the terrible damage that has been done. Her language is often quite bitter, e.g. "the blowback from some old story". At the end though, she seems hopeful for the future when she talks about spring returning and the "first break of blue".

Q5. • This line might be set apart from the rest to emphasise the feeling of hope it contains. It also seems to show how small the hope is compared to the enormity of the rest of the disaster.

Page 31 — Crossing the Loch

Q1. a) • I think the narrator is talking to a friend who went with her on the trip across the loch.

b) • The narrator's use of words like "we" and "us" makes the poem sound personal and intimate, but it excludes the reader slightly because we know that she is not talking to us.

Q2.
•

Image	Mood	Effect
"cold shawl of breeze"	threatening	unsettling image because shawls are usually warm
"small boat of saints"	magical	image sounds special and otherworldly
"jumped / to draw the boat safe"	relieved	sounds like the people were happy to have made it

Q3. • I picture the loch as a large lake surrounded by hills. Images such as "the loch's / phosphorescence" make it sound like an exciting and mysterious place, but the "hunched hills" and "ticking nuclear hulls"

The Answers

Q4. • The questions suggest that the narrator is unable to remember all the details of the trip, possibly because it was such a long time ago. They also have the effect of drawing the reader into the poem.

Q5. • I think the poet is writing about a trip that took place in her own youth and that is important to her. Perhaps she wanted to relive a time when she was young, adventurous and carefree because now she is older and can't do "foolhardy" things any more.

Page 33 — Hard Water

Q1. • Sprackland makes the Welsh water sound silly and lighthearted, but describes the hard water as being "straight" and down-to-earth.

Q2. • "Honest water"
• "blunt"
• "frankness"
• "It tasted of work"

Q3. • The town sounds industrial, e.g. "cooling towers" and quite harsh, e.g. "pitiless nights". It also sounds like a hard-working place, e.g. "the true taste / of early mornings".

Q4. a) • The water seems to remind the narrator of home. She feels rooted in the area because of it. It gives her a sense of identity and belonging.

b) • The lines make the narrator sound proud to belong to the area she describes, even though it is not very glamorous and life sounds like it can sometimes be hard. Perhaps the town, like the water, is both "fierce" and "lovely" and this is what attracts her to it.

Q5. • I think the poet chose to write about hard water because it reminds her so much of home. The water also shares several characteristics with her local area and the people who live there. This makes it ideal to sum up the things she loves best about her home town.

Section Three

Pages 34-35 — Place

Q1. a) • Mountain, lake, town, island, home

b) • Love, fear, confusion, sadness, excitement

Q2. a) • My favourite place is my grandparents' garden. It is long and rambling with a tumble-down summer house hidden in the rose bed at the far end. It is a special place because I spent so much of my childhood there, playing football on the grass with my grandad, or having tea parties in the summer house with my sister. Whenever I come here I feel warm and safe. The place is full of happy memories, but I sometimes feel sad when I think of my grandad, who died a few years ago.

b) • I think 'The Blackbird of Glanmore' relates most closely to my feelings about my favourite place. The narrator in this poem has happy memories of Glanmore, like his brother "Cavorting through the yard", but he also has sad memories because of his brother's death.

Q3. a) • passion — 'Storm in the Black Forest' — "tumbling wriggling down the sky"
• joy — 'Below the Green Corrie' — "My life was enriched / with an infusion of theirs"
• fear — 'Wind' — "we grip /Our hearts"
• nostalgia — 'The Wild Swans at Coole' — "The nineteenth autumn has come upon me"
• awe — 'The Prelude' — "huge and mighty forms"
• anger — 'London' — "Every black'ning church appalls"
• uncertainty — 'Cold Knap Lake' — "Was I there?"

b) • 'The Blackbird of Glanmore' — happiness, thoughtfulness

c) • The feeling of thoughtfulness in the poem is consistent with the poem's sadness — it is the narrator's reflection on his brother's death that makes him sad. The happiness does seem to be a contradiction, but it is understandable. It comes from the blackbird and thoughts of his brother before the accident, as a lively little boy dancing in the yard.

Q4.
•

Storm in the Black Forest	Crossing the Loch
Forest at twilight	A loch late at night
Storm	A boat trip across the loch with friends
Irregular line lengths with no fixed rhythm or rhyme — seems chaotic like a storm; enjambment emphasises narrator's excitement	First person narration sounds personal; no regular rhythm or rhyme makes it sound natural and conversational
Vivid, colourful images — "gold-bronze flutters", "pure white liquid"; repetition emphasises excitement	Trip made to sound magical and thrilling — "loch's phosphorescence", "small boat of saints"

Q5. a) • 'Hard Water' presents a positive attitude towards a place. This is reflected in the poet's use of local dialect phrases, like "hey up me duck", which celebrate the town's people and culture.

b) • The narrator seems proud of the town she comes from and fond of the people who live there.

Q6. • In 'London', the narrator is clearly angry and appalled by the poverty and misery faced by the city. When he says things like "Runs in blood down palace walls", he seems bitter that those in power do nothing to help. This is very different to the narrator of 'Hard Water' who loves the urban environment of her home town, however hard and industrial: "I loved coming home to this".

Pages 36-37 — Nature

Q1. a) • 'The Blackbird of Glanmore', 'The Wild Swans at Coole', 'Below the Green Corrie', 'The Prelude', 'The Moment', 'Spellbound', 'Storm in the Black Forest', 'Wind', 'Cold Knap Lake', 'Crossing the Loch', 'Price We Pay for the Sun', 'Neighbours'

b) • I think poets write about nature because it influences so many aspects of all our lives. Diversity in nature inspires strong and wide-ranging feelings — everything from happiness to fear.

Q2. "Winds stampeding the fields" = 'Wind'; "The giant trees are bending" = 'Spellbound'; "mountains gathered round me / like bandits" = 'Below the Green Corrie'; "cliffs fissure and collapse" = 'The Moment'; "a huge peak, black and huge" = 'The Prelude'.

Q3. a) • awe, fear, respect, excitement, love

b) • I think that the most common feeling is awe of nature. The narrator in 'The Prelude' fears nature, the narrator of 'Below the Green Corrie' celebrates it, and the speaker in 'Spellbound' is enchanted by it — but they are all in awe of its power and they all imply that nature should be respected.

Q4.
•

The Prelude	The Moment
Long narrative in the first person allows narrator to explore his feelings about nature; blank verse	No regular rhythm or rhyme makes the poem sound clear and powerful
Nature is described as pretty and non-threatening at first, but becomes dark and sinister as the mountain is personified	Nature is first shown to be violent, then calm and quietly in control
Confidence changes to fear and uncertainty; view of nature turned upside down by the encounter with the peak	Nature is powerful and angry; human beings are made to seem weak and arrogant in comparison

Q5. • The humans in 'The Moment' are described as arrogant, believing that they "own" everything around them — but really, nature is just waiting to come and take it all back. The

6

The Answers

message of this poem seems to be that nature is extremely powerful and should be respected. A human is merely a "visitor" in nature's world.

Q6. a) • 'Storm in a Black Forest' is about the power of nature. The lines and stanzas are irregular and chaotic, just like the chaos of the storm.

b) • The poet uses onomatopoeia to capture the sounds of the storm. Words like "cackle" capture the noise of the thunder, giving it a harsh, unnatural sound.

c) • The narrator is excited by the storm. He is in awe of its brilliance and power. He is also scornful of mankind's belief that they can harness that power for their own use — "This is the electricity that man is supposed to have mastered... / supposed to!". He clearly feels that we underestimate the power of nature.

Q7. a) • 'Wind' is about the power of nature over defenceless human beings. 'Spellbound' has a similar theme. In it, the narrator talks about being captivated by a powerful storm. The storm is controlling her and preventing her from finding shelter and safety.

b) • In 'Wind', the poet uses powerful visual metaphors, such as "wind that dented the balls of my eyes" to present the power and violence of nature and the pain it causes. He also plays with sound, using the onomatopoeic "booming" and "crashing" to convey the noise of the wind. In 'Spellbound', the regular rhythm and ABAB rhyme make the poem sound like a spell. This conveys the powerful magic of the storm. Alliteration, e.g. "wild winds" also adds to this feeling.

c) • I like the poem 'Wind' because its vivid imagery makes the storm easy to visualise. We also get a real feel for the fear and vulnerability of the people in the house.

Page 38 — Memory

Q1. a) • 'Crossing the Loch' — "we watched water shine / on our fingers and oars"

b) • 'The Blackbird of Glanmore' — "And I think of one gone to him"

Q2. a) • sadness, contemplation, weariness, nostalgia

b) • 'The Blackbird of Glanmore' — sadness, pain, contemplation, happiness, love. The lists are quite similar; both poems have feelings of sadness and contemplation, but 'The Blackbird of Glanmore' contrasts these feelings with those of love and happiness.

Q3. • 'Cold Knap Lake' and 'Crossing the Loch' both present the idea that memories can be unreliable.

The narrators of both poems ask rhetorical questions, e.g. "Was I there?", "Who rowed, and who kept their peace?". These show that they doubt their memories or are uncertain of particular details. 'Cold Knap Lake' also uses vague, dreamlike language to show that the narrator's memories are fuzzy and unclear, e.g. "shadowy","cloudiness".

Q4. a) • In 'Crossing the Loch', the narrator is remembering a boat trip across a loch that took place in her youth.

b) • The trip is made to sound like a magical and otherworldly experience. She talks about the water's "phosphorescence" and being in "a small boat of saints". The narrator has long since grown up, but she still remembers the trip. In the final stanza, she sounds nostalgic for a time when she was carefree and adventurous.

Q5. a) • 'The Blackbird of Glanmore' has a strong link between memory and place. Glanmore is the narrator's home — seeing the blackbird there triggers memories of his younger brother "Cavorting through the yard" before he died. It reminds him of the sadness that is linked to the house.

b) Both memories are linked to a particular place and time, but the emotions involved are different. In 'The Blackbird of Glanmore', the narrator's memories are tinged with sadness about his "lost brother". In 'Crossing the Loch', the narrator remembers her excitement as they "watched water shine", but also the fear she felt during the trip.

Page 39 — Sadness

Q1. a) • 'The Wild Swans at Coole', 'Neighbours'

b) • The narrator in 'The Wild Swans at Coole' is sad about his lost youth and the opportunities he has missed in life. The narrator in 'Neighbours' is sad about the aftermath of the Chernobyl nuclear accident and its effects on nature.

c) • I can relate to the sadness in 'Neighbours'. There was recently an oil spill on a beach near our house. It took a long time to clear up and destroyed a lot of wildlife in the process. It was sad seeing all the seabirds with oil in their feathers. The beach is only just returning to normal now. We know the effects of Chernobyl also lasted a long time when the narrator talks about the damage in both "That spring" and "This spring".

Q2. a) • melancholy, sorrowful, cheerless, desolate, dispirited

b) • melancholy — 'The Wild Swans at Coole'; sorrowful — 'The Blackbird of Glanmore';

cheerless — 'A Vision'; desolate — 'London'; dispirited — 'Neighbours'

Q3. a) • 'London' uses emotive images that contrast innocence with horror to convey the misery in the city, e.g. "In every infant's cry of fear". 'The Blackbird of Glanmore' also uses emotive images. The poet chooses to contrast life and death in "stillness dancer" and "Haunter-son" to emphasise his sadness over his brother's death.

b) • 'The Blackbird of Glanmore' is narrated in the first person, which makes the sadness seem more personal. It has no regular rhyme scheme or rhythm, which makes it sound like natural speech. Because it sounds so real and heartfelt, we empathise more with the narrator's feelings. In contrast, 'London' does have a regular rhyme scheme and rhythm. This helps to stress the city's unrelenting misery. Again, first person narration makes the poem sound personal and therefore more believable.

Page 40 — Uncertainty

Q1. a) • 'The Prelude', 'Cold Knap Lake', 'The Moment', 'Price We Pay for the Sun', 'Neighbours'

b) • 'The Prelude' — the world around him; 'Cold Knap Lake' — the reliability of memory; 'The Moment' — our place in the world; 'Price We Pay for the Sun' — her feelings towards the islands; 'Neighbours' — the nature of the disaster, what will happen in the future.

Q2. a) • When I first started secondary school I felt really uncertain about where to go and what I should be doing. I had just moved to a new area, so I did not really know anyone and the school seemed huge. I felt lost and nervous most of the time.

b) • I can empathise with the narrator in 'The Prelude'. When I was at primary school I was confident and had lots of friends, but when I first moved to my secondary school I felt shy and quite lonely. A similar change happens to the narrator in this poem. He is also afraid of the mountain's size — I was a bit afraid of my new school's size too.

Q3. a) • In 'Cold Knap Lake', the narrator asks herself the question, "Was I there?" to convey her uncertainty as to the reliability of her memory. Her language becomes dreamy and vague, e.g. "satiny mud blooms". She also sounds troubled in places, for example when she says, "treading, heavy webs of swans".

b) • The poet uses enjambment in lines 16 to 20, so that her sentence is long and trailing. It makes the narrator

Answers

The Answers

sound thoughtful and unsure of what she is saying.

Q4. a) • In 'London', the narrator is very certain of his feelings about the city, e.g. "Every black'ning church appalls". He is angry and horrified by the conditions there.

b) • In 'London', the narrator's language is dramatic and confident. He uses powerful images and hyperbole to emphasise his point, e.g. "blights with plagues the marriage hearse". This is a big contrast to the dreamlike phrases in the penultimate stanza of 'Cold Knap Lake'.

Page 41 — Relationships

Q1. a) • 'Below the Green Corrie'

b) • 'Price We Pay for the Sun'

Q2. • In 'Below the Green Corrie', the narrator's relationship with the mountains goes through different stages. At first the mountains are dangerous and threatening, they "gathered round" him like bandits, "full of thunders". But then the narrator takes control of the relationship and the mountains share their lives with him. Finally, the narrator shows his respect for the mountains when he turns to "look goodbye".

Q3. • I can relate to the narrator's relationship with her home town in 'Hard Water'. I am really proud to come from Edinburgh — I love all aspects of the city and the people there.

Q4. a) • 'Price We Pay for the Sun' is about the relationship the narrator has with the Caribbean islands she grew up around.

b) • The narrator seems proud to come from these islands and celebrates their culture. She also seems to feel a sense of loyalty, defending them against the tourists' stereotypical views. But the islands are also a place of pain and suffering for her and she appears to have conflicting feelings about them.

c) • The narrator links the islands with her family to show how important they are to her: "my mother's breasts / like sleeping volcanoes". But her use of violent natural imagery, such as "volcanoes" and "hurricanes", also shows us they are a place of pain.

Page 42 — Passion

Q1. a) • 'London'

b) • 'Storm in the Black Forest'

Q2. "jugfull after jugfull of pure white liquid fire" — 'Storm in the Black Forest'; "mind-forged manacles" — 'London'; "the stones cry out under the horizons" — 'Wind'; "I cannot, cannot go" — 'Spellbound'; "fierce

lovely water that marked me for life" — 'Hard Water'.

Q3. a) • 'Storm in the Black Forest' is a passionate poem about a storm. The narrator is captivated and excited by the storm's power. He is also extremely scornful about man's belief that he can control nature, which is a less positive emotion.

b) • The poet uses a lot of repetition to convey the narrator's intense excitement over the storm, e.g. "pure white... bright white / ...still brighter white", which makes his descriptions sound spontaneous and natural.

Q4.
•

	London	Hard Water
	Dramatic monologue written in quatrains; regular rhythm and ABAB rhyme scheme.	First person narration; no regular rhyme scheme or rhythm.
	Dramatic, emotive images, e.g. "every infant's cry of fear"	Dialect; blunt, down-to-earth descriptions — "Honest water, bright and not quite clean"
	Angry at the state of the city and the ambivalence of those in power	Fierce pride and affection for her home town

Page 43 — Hope

Q1. • I hoped for a new camera for my birthday last year and was really pleased when my parents bought me one. I had been trying to persuade them for months!

Q2. a) • 'The Blackbird of Glanmore', 'Neighbours'

b) • 'The Blackbird of Glanmore' — "In front of my house of life"; 'Neighbours' — "first break of blue"

Q3. a) • 'Wind', 'London', 'A Vision'

b) • 'A Vision' contrasts the hope and excitement of the old plans with the bleak reality of the present. This enforces his message that all hope for the future is now "fully extinct". 'Wind' on the other hand simply leaves us with no sign that the storm is coming to an end. The stones still "cry out" in pain and the humans can do nothing but sit it out.

Q4. • I think that Armitage makes a good point when he suggests that architects need to take into consideration the lives of real people when drawing their plans, otherwise their ideas will not work. I can also empathise with the people in 'Wind' who feel utterly helpless against the storm's power. I don't agree with Armitage's implication that there is no hope for the future though. I think people can learn from past mistakes to come up with more effective plans for future towns.

Section Four

Page 45 — Adding Quotes and Developing Points

Answer Extract 1
• (A) "I loved coming home to this"
• (B) "The wild winds coldly blow"

Answer Extract 2
• (A) "hey up me duck"
• (B) "I cannot, cannot go"

Page 46 — Adding Quotes and Developing Points

Answer Extract 3
• (A) However it seems that it is the town's ordinariness and down-to-earth nature that attract her to it. She clearly values the qualities that come from the town's industrial nature, for example "straight talk" and hard work.

• (B) In contrast to Sprackland, it is the excitement and thrill of the storm, despite its danger, that attracts Brontë to the place in her poem. It is magical and otherworldly and this is what draws her to it.

Sample Plan
• (A) "those brilliant creatures"
• (B) "The nineteenth autumn has come upon me"
• (C) "Their leader / swaggered up close"
• (D) I sympathise with the narrator of this poem and the sadness he feels about growing older. His love for the swans and the lake at Coole really comes across.
• (E) I agree with the narrator's point of view that while nature can be wonderful and exciting, it can also be dangerous. By treating it with respect, the narrator finds that nature enriches his life.

Page 47 — Marking Answer Extracts

Answer Extract 5
• I think that this answer would get a grade B because it talks about the themes of the poems and explores how their language affects the reader. The ideas are backed up with examples. To get a grade A it would need to give other possible interpretations of the language and compare the poems more closely.

The Answers

Page 48 — Marking Answer Extracts

Answer Extract 6

- I think that this answer would get a grade A because it compares the two poems in detail, giving plenty of evidence for its ideas. It explores the impact of language on the reader and considers a variety of meanings for the two poems. A complete answer would need to include more on form and structure and their effect on the reader.

Page 49 — Marking Answer Extracts

Answer Extract 7

- I think that this answer would get a grade B because it compares the two poems and focuses closely on their use of language. It also uses quotations to support ideas. To get a grade A it would need to say more about how the language affects the reader as well as comparing the poems more closely.

Page 50 — Marking a Complete Answer

Answer 8

- I think this answer would get a grade A because it covers a range of different interpretations and focuses closely on the effect of language, form and structure on the reader. It also uses plenty of evidence to support ideas. It could be improved by talking about less obvious things like the effect of personification in 'The Prelude' and coming up with a couple more original points.

ISBN 978 1 84762 540 3

9 781847 625403

APHA41